Developing Num

MENTAL MATHS

ACTIVITIES FOR THE DAILY MATHS LESSON

year 4

Hilary Koll and Steve Mills

A & C BLACK

Contents

Mental calculation strategies (x and ÷)

Published 2004 by A & C Black Publishers Limited
37 Soho Square, London W1D 3QZ
www.acblack.com

ISBN 0-7136-6913-6

Copyright text © Hilary Koll and Steve Mills, 2004
Copyright illustrations © David Benham, 2004
Copyright cover illustration © Charlotte Hard, 2004
Editors: Lynne Williamson and Marie Lister

The authors and publishers would like to thank Jane McNeill and Catherine Yemm for their advice in producing this series of books.

A CIP catalogue record for this book is available from the British Library.

Printed and bound in Great Britain by Cromwell Press Ltd, Trowbridge.

A & C Black uses paper produced with elemental chlorine-free pulp, harvested from managed sustainable forests.

Introduction

Developing Numeracy: Mental Maths is a series of seven photocopiable activity books designed to be used during the daily maths lesson. This book focuses on the skills and concepts for mental maths outlined in the National Numeracy Strategy *Framework for teaching mathematics* for Year 4. The activities are intended to be used in the time allocated to pupil activities; they aim to reinforce the knowledge and develop the facts, skills and understanding explored during the main part of the lesson. They provide practice and consolidation of the objectives contained in the framework document.

Mental Maths Year 4

To calculate mentally with confidence, it is necessary to understand the three main aspects of numeracy shown in the diagram below. These underpin the teaching of specific mental calculation strategies.

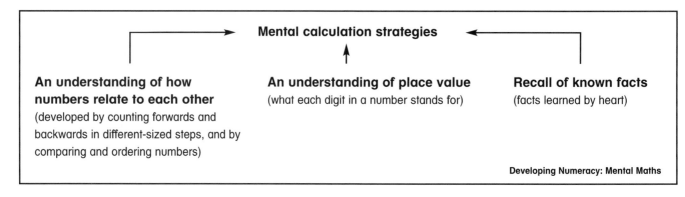

Year 4 supports the teaching of mental maths by providing a series of activities which develop these essential skills. On the whole the activities are designed for children to work on independently, although this is not always possible and occasionally some children may need support.

Year 4 develops concepts and skills for the different aspects of numeracy in the following ways:

An understanding of how numbers relate to each other

- recognising and extending number sequences formed by counting from any number in steps of constant size.

An understanding of place value

- knowing what each digit represents in whole numbers to at least 10 000;
- adding/subtracting 1, 10, 100 or 1000 to/from any integer;
- reading and writing the vocabulary of comparing and ordering numbers, and giving one or more numbers lying between two given numbers;
- using symbols correctly, including less than (<) and greater than (>).

Recall of known facts

Know by heart or derive quickly:
- addition and subtraction facts for all numbers to 20;
- all number pairs with a total of 100;
- all pairs of multiples of 50 with a total of 1000;

- multiplication facts for the 2, 3, 4, 5 and 10 times tables and the corresponding division facts, and beginning to know the facts for the 6, 7, 8 and 9 times tables;
- doubles of all whole numbers to 50;
- doubles of multiples of 10 to 500 and doubles of multiples of 100 to 5000, and the corresponding halves.

Mental calculation strategies

- finding a small difference by counting up;
- partitioning into tens and units, adding the tens first;
- identifying near doubles, using doubles already known;
- adding or subtracting the nearest multiple of 10, then adjusting;
- adding three or four small numbers, and three two-digit multiples of 10;
- checking the sum of several numbers by adding in reverse order;
- using known number facts and place value to add mentally, including any pair of two-digit whole numbers;
- using doubling, starting from known facts;
- using known number facts and place value to multiply integers, including by 10;
- using closely related facts (for example, multiplying by 9 or 11 by multiplying by 10, then adjusting);
- partitioning when multiplying;
- finding remainders after division, and using known number facts and place value to divide.

Extension

Many of the activity sheets end with a challenge (**Now try this!**) which reinforces and extends the children's learning, and provides the teacher with an opportunity for assessment. On occasion it may be helpful to read the instructions with the children before they begin the activity. For some of the challenges the children will need to record their answers on a separate piece of paper.

Organisation

Very little equipment is needed, but it will be useful to have the following resources available: coloured pencils, counters, dice, scissors, number lines and number tracks.

To help teachers select appropriate learning experiences for the children, the activities are grouped into sections within the book. However, the activities are not expected to be used in this order; the sheets are intended to support, rather than direct, the teacher's planning.

Some activities can be made easier or more challenging by masking or substituting numbers. You may wish to re-use some pages by copying them onto card and laminating them.

Teachers' notes

Brief notes are provided at the foot of each page giving ideas and suggestions for maximising the effectiveness of the activity sheets. These can be masked before copying.

Whole-class warm-up activities

The following activities provide some practical ideas which can be used to introduce the main teaching part of the lesson.

Question boxes

Draw two rectangles on the board. Inside the first rectangle, write the numbers 30, 20, 18, 15, 12, 8, 5, 2. Inside the other, write 150, 120, 50, 38, 33, 17, 15, 12, 10, 6, 4, 3. Ask the children to choose two numbers from the first box and use them in any type of calculation to make a number in the second box: for example, 30 – 18 = 12; 18 + 15 = 33; 30 ÷ 5 = 6.

Bingo

Ask the children to draw a 4 × 3 grid and to write a number between 0 and 30 in each of the 12 boxes. (Explain that all the numbers must be different.) Call out questions with answers that lie between 0 and 30: for example, *7 times 4* or *15 minus 7*. Any children who have the answers in their grids may cross them out. The winner is the first player to cross out all 12 numbers. Keep a record of the questions asked, so that you can check the winner's grid and see which questions cause difficulty.

Targets

Write several numbers on the board, such as 80, 50, 9, 6, 4, and a target number, such as 244. Set the children the challenge of hitting the target number, or getting as close as possible to it, using some or all of the numbers and whatever operations they wish. A solution to this example is: 9 – 6 = 3, 3 × 80 = 240, and 240 + 4 = 244.

Function machines

Draw a simple machine on the board and write a single-step or multi-step operation inside it, such as '– 12' or '– 6 × 5'. Say a number, such as 20, and ask for the output number after the rule has been applied.

Function machines can also be used in the following ways:
- give the output number and ask the children for the input number that produces it;
- give pairs of input and output numbers that correspond to the same rule, and ask the children to work out the rule. For example, for the rule '× 4 + 2', you could give the following pairs: 3 and 14, 5 and 22, 7 and 30. Rather than revealing the rule to the rest of the class when they have worked it out, the children could suggest further pairs of input and output numbers that correspond to the rule.

Make it

Draw a 6 × 6 grid on the board containing the numbers 1 to 36. (Alternatively, draw a poster-sized grid and cover it with acetate.) Then write three numbers between 1 and 6 on the board, such as 5, 2 and 3. Ask the children to use these three numbers to make as many of the numbers on the grid as possible: for example, 5 + 2 + 3 = 10; 5 – 2 + 3 = 6; 5 × 2 + 6 = 16. Cross out these numbers. When the combinations are exhausted, write three more numbers on the board and continue. The aim is to cross out all the numbers in the grid.

Sophie's secrets

Sanjay keys a number into the calculator.

Sophie secretly adds or subtracts a number to or from it.

- **In your head, work out what Sophie adds or subtracts.**

1. + 1000   5938   6938

2.   2684   2694

3.   6367   6267

4.   9453   9454

5.   3275   2275

6.   3637   3636

7.   4968   5068

8.   2796   2806

9.   4993   4994

10.   2096   1996

11.   3705   3695

12.   2806   3806

- **Count on from the number shown:**

Now try this!

in 1s	2759	____ ____ ____ ____ ____
in 10s	2759	____ ____ ____ ____ ____
in 100s	2759	____ ____ ____ ____ ____
in 1000s	2759	____ ____ ____ ____ ____
in 10s	7965	____ ____ ____ ____ ____
in 100s	9421	____ ____ ____ ____ ____

Teachers' note At the start of the lesson, practise counting in steps of 1, 10, 100 and 1000 from any three- or four-digit number up to 10 000. When comparing the pairs of numbers in this activity, some children may find it helpful to use place value (arrow) cards to partition the numbers.

**Developing Numeracy
Mental Maths Year 4
© A & C BLACK**

6

All change

To multiply by 100, move the digits two places to the left. Put zeros in the empty columns.

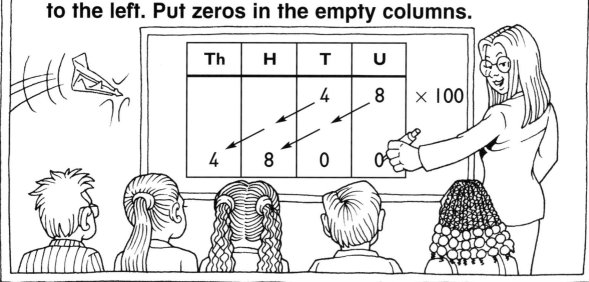

1. Change these prices from pounds to pence. Multiply by 100.

£2 = ___200___ p   £5 = _____ p   £9 = _____ p

£34 = _____ p   £27 = _____ p   £48 = _____ p

£121 = _____ p   £260 = _____ p   £306 = _____ p

2. Change these lengths from metres to centimetres. Multiply by 100.

4 m = ___400___ cm   7 m = _____ cm   8 m = _____ cm

62 m = _____ cm   74 m = _____ cm   97 m = _____ cm

630 m = _____ cm   105 m = _____ cm   630 m = _____ cm

• **Change these amounts. You will need to** boxed:divide **by 100.**

400p = £___4___   600p = £_____   1100p = £_____

6700p = £_____   8300p = £_____   95 300p = £_____

2500 cm = ___25___ m   5300 cm = _____ m   4900 cm = _____ m

66 400 cm = _____ m   10 100 cm = _____ m   22 000 cm = _____ m

Teachers' note It is important that the children appreciate that it is the digits that move to the left or right when multiplying or dividing by 10 or 100, and that zeros are used as place holders to indicate the columns that are empty.

**Developing Numeracy
Mental Maths Year 4
© A & C BLACK**

Pop concert

The seat numbers go up in ones.

1. Fill in the missing numbers.

567	568				572
1696					1701
2098					2104
3997					4003

2. Write the seat numbers in these rows.

1094	_____ _____ _____ _____ _____ _____	1101
4726	_____ _____ _____ _____ _____ _____	4733
3096	_____ _____ _____ _____ _____ _____	3103

- Write $<$ or $>$ between each pair of numbers to make a true statement.
- Then write all the [multiples of 10] that lie between.

| 7465 | $<$ | 7482 |
| 7470, 7480 |

| 5021 | | 4995 |
| _____ |

| 8016 | | 7989 |
| _____ |

| 2122 | | 2099 |
| _____ |

| 7702 | | 7677 |
| _____ |

| 3079 | | 3109 |
| _____ |

Teachers' note At the start of the lesson, introduce or revise the 'greater than' and 'less than' signs. Give pairs of four-digit numbers and encourage the children to say all the numbers that lie between them. For the extension activity, revise the word 'multiple' if necessary.

Developing Numeracy
Mental Maths Year 4
© A & C BLACK

Follow the trail

- **Find the total length of each trail.**

1. Each matchstick is 5 cm long. Count in **fives**.

2. Each needle is 4 cm long. Count in **fours**.

3. Each pin is 3 cm long. Count in **threes**.

Discuss with a partner how you could check your answers.

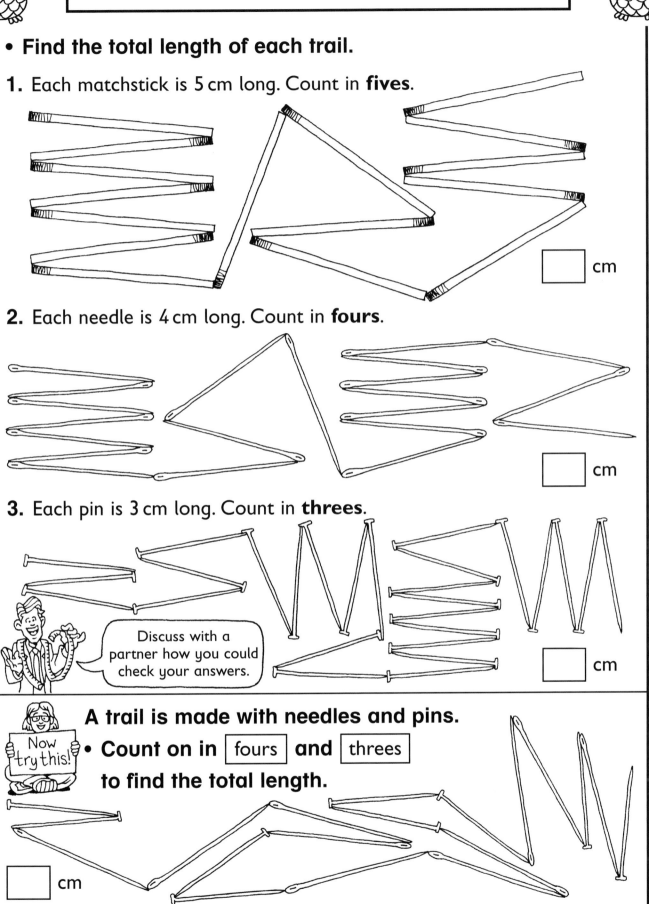

$\boxed{}$ cm

$\boxed{}$ cm

$\boxed{}$ cm

Now try this!

A trail is made with needles and pins.

- **Count on in** $\boxed{\text{fours}}$ **and** $\boxed{\text{threes}}$ **to find the total length.**

$\boxed{}$ cm

- **Sketch three different trails with a length of** $\boxed{47\,\text{cm}}$.

Teachers' note Watch out for children counting on using their fingers – instead encourage them to use their knowledge of number bonds and to bridge through multiples of 10 (in examples such as '17 count on 4'). To check their answers, the children could count back from the answer in steps of the appropriate size.

**Developing Numeracy
Mental Maths Year 4
© A & C BLACK**

Arctic antics

- **Follow the arrows and count back in** $\boxed{25s}$ **until you reach** $\boxed{-100}$ **. Fill in all the ice blocks, following the different routes.**

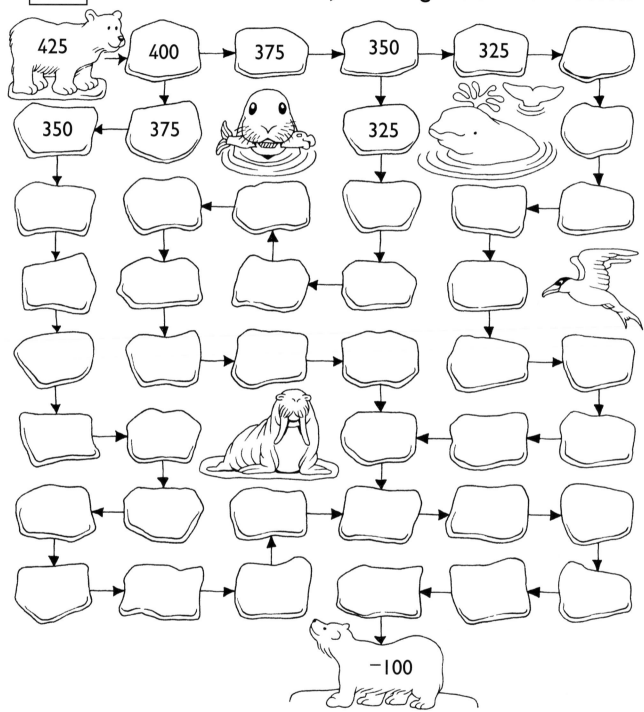

425 400 375 350 325

350 375 325

- **Check each route by counting up from ⁻100 to 425.**

- **If a polar bear travels 25 km each day looking for food, how far does it travel in 13 days? _____ km**

Count in 25s to find out.

Teachers' note Ensure the children realise that there are several routes that separate and join at various points. Encourage them to check their answers using the numbers from other routes and by counting up from ⁻100 along different routes. They could draw lines in different colours to show the routes they have checked.

Developing Numeracy Mental Maths Year 4 © A & C BLACK

10

Adults are odd!

In a fancy-dress fun run, adults wear ⬛ odd ⬛ numbers and children wear ⬛ even ⬛ numbers.

• Write the next four ⬛ odd ⬛ numbers in each sequence.

1.	33	35	37	39	41				
2.	121	123	125	127	129				
3.	155	157	159	161	163				
4.	201	203	205	207	209				
5.	349	351	353	355	357				
6.	389	391	393	395	397				

• Write the next five ⬛ even ⬛ numbers in each sequence.

7.	64	66	68	70					
8.	88	90	92	94					
9.	104	106	108	110					
10.	150	152	154	156					
11.	292	294	296	298					
12.	388	390	392	394					

Now try this!

• Write whether each number belongs to an adult or a child.

Remember, adults are odd!

426	child	371	_____	469	_____
770	_____	432	_____	605	_____

Teachers' note At the start of the lesson, practise counting in twos from any two- or three-digit number, drawing attention to the pattern of digits for odd and even numbers.

Developing Numeracy
Mental Maths Year 4
© A & C BLACK

Cube views

Ben puts towers of cubes together to make a model. He writes on top of each tower how many cubes there are. Then he draws the view of the top of the model.

● **Write the total number of cubes in each model.**

| 6 | 2 | 8 | 7 | 9 | ___ | 6 | 7 | ___ |

| 2 | 5 | 9 | ___ | 6 | 3 | 6 | ___ | 5 | 2 | 7 | ___ |

| 3 | 2 | 5 | ___ | 1 | 3 | 8 | ___ | 1 | 6 | 4 | ___ |
| 2 | | | | 6 | | | | 7 | | | |

| 11 | 4 | ___ | 13 | 6 | ___ | 17 | 2 | ___ |

| 14 | 2 | ___ | 3 | 16 | ___ | 4 | 8 | ___ |
| 4 | | | 1 | | | 5 | | |

| 8 | 2 | 8 | ___ | 7 | 6 | 6 | ___ | 11 | 5 | 1 | ___ |
| 1 | | | | 1 | | | | 1 | | | |

Now try this!

● **Fill in numbers so that each model has a total of** 18 .

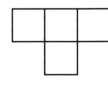

| 9 | 9 |

**Developing Numeracy
Mental Maths Year 4
© A & C BLACK**

Teachers' note At the start of the lesson, discuss addition facts of numbers up to 20, including doubles and near doubles. Remind the children that numbers can be added in any order and invite them to suggest strategies for finding the total of several numbers, including recalling number pairs that total 9, 10 or 11. Demonstrate practically how models can be made using towers of cubes.

Slimy subtraction facts

- **Find the length of each worm by subtracting the start number from the end number.**

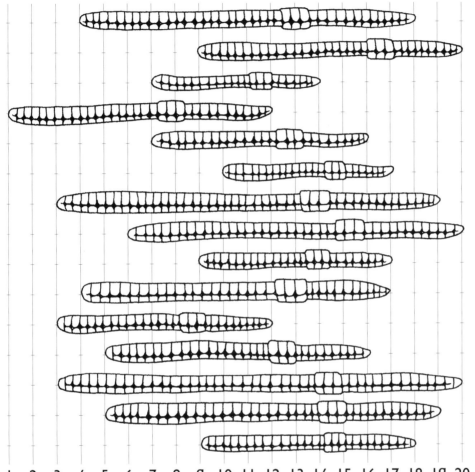

18 – 4 = 14	
20 – 9 =	

- **Answer these subtractions.**

1. 18 – 5 = ___   **2.** 16 – 8 = ___   **3.** 19 – 12 = ___   **4.** 17 – 6 = ___

5. 20 – 7 = ___   **6.** 18 – 3 = ___   **7.** 17 – 8 = ___   **8.** 16 – 9 = ___

- **Write the start and end numbers of all the worms you could draw with a length of 8.**

Use whole numbers between **0** and **20**.

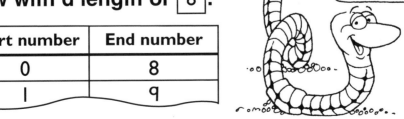

Example:

Start number	End number
0	8
1	9

Teachers' note Demonstrate how to read the start and end number of each worm, and discuss strategies for subtracting, such as counting back or counting up. Encourage the children to use rapid recall and to learn the subtraction facts by heart. At the end of the lesson, reinforce the facts that the children found most difficult to learn.

Developing Numeracy
Mental Maths Year 4
© A & C BLACK

The path to true love

Who is Princess Tia's true love?

- **Start in the centre of the maze. Find a way out by looping pairs of** adjacent **numbers with a total of** 100 .

> **Adjacent** means next to each other.

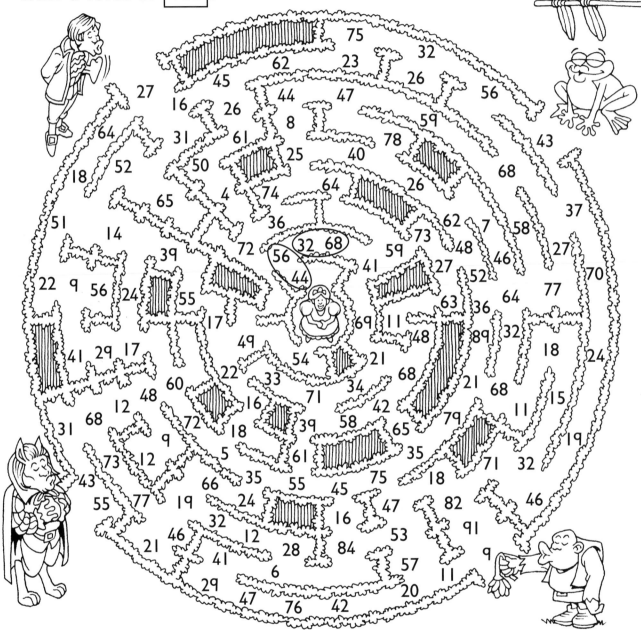

- **Fill in the missing numbers.**

$100 - 73 = \boxed{}$ $100 - 31 = \boxed{}$ $100 - 88 = \boxed{}$

$100 - \boxed{} = 44$ $100 - \boxed{} = 62$ $100 - \boxed{} = 77$

$36 + \boxed{} = 100$ $43 + \boxed{} = 100$ $28 + \boxed{} = 100$

> Now try this!

Teachers' note Remind the children that the units digits will add to make 10, so the tens digits must total 90 only. Watch out for children making mistakes such as 43 + 67 = 100.

Developing Numeracy Mental Maths Year 4 © A & C BLACK

The Invisible Man

The Invisible Man is experimenting. He starts with a **full** 1000 ml bottle of potion **each time** and drinks some of it.

- Write how much potion is left in the bottle, if he drinks:

1. 150 ml
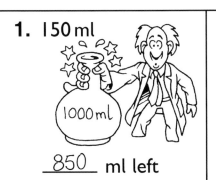
__850__ ml left

2. 300 ml
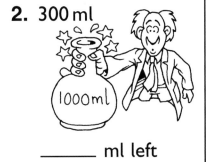
_____ ml left

3. 950 ml

_____ ml left

4. 750 ml
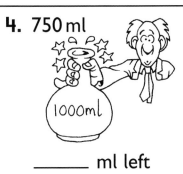
_____ ml left

5. 800 ml

_____ ml left

6. 550 ml

_____ ml left

7. 350 ml
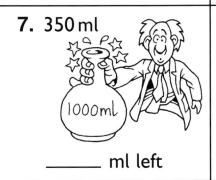
_____ ml left

8. 250 ml
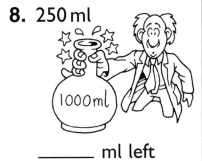
_____ ml left

9. 50 ml
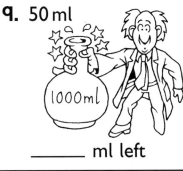
_____ ml left

10. 400 ml
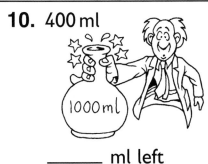
_____ ml left

11. 700 ml
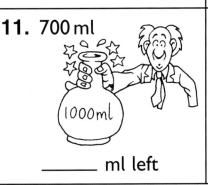
_____ ml left

12. 450 ml

_____ ml left

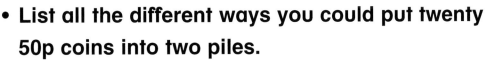

- **List all the different ways you could put twenty 50p coins into two piles.**

Example: 50p and £9.50

Teachers' note Encourage the children to use their knowledge of number pairs with a total of 10 or 100 (for example, 4 + 6 = 10 and 40 + 60 = 100 so 400 + 600 = 1000). Point out that when adding numbers ending in 50, the tens digits add to make 100, so the hundreds must total 900. Watch out for children making mistakes such as 450 + 650 = 1000.

**Developing Numeracy
Mental Maths Year 4
© A & C BLACK**

Mountain heights

- **Count on from the smaller number to find the difference in height.**

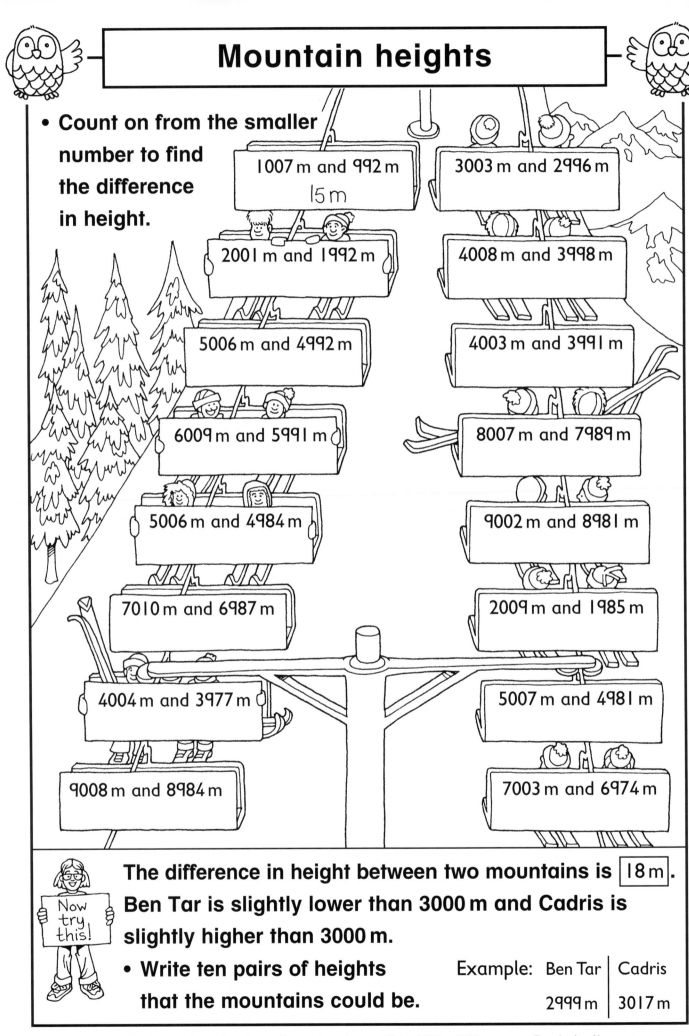

1007 m and 992 m
15 m

3003 m and 2996 m

2001 m and 1992 m

4008 m and 3998 m

5006 m and 4992 m

4003 m and 3991 m

6009 m and 5991 m

8007 m and 7989 m

5006 m and 4984 m

9002 m and 8981 m

7010 m and 6987 m

2009 m and 1985 m

4004 m and 3977 m

5007 m and 4981 m

9008 m and 8984 m

7003 m and 6974 m

The difference in height between two mountains is $\boxed{18\,\text{m}}$. **Ben Tar is slightly lower than 3000 m and Cadris is slightly higher than 3000 m.**

- **Write ten pairs of heights that the mountains could be.**

Now try this!

Example:	Ben Tar	Cadris
	2999 m	3017 m

Teachers' note Revise counting on from the smaller number using a multiple of 100 or 1000 as a stopover (using examples such as 902 – 897 or 5008 – 4989). The children might need to sketch number lines or make other jottings to work out the differences. Encourage them to be systematic when completing the extension activity.

**Developing Numeracy
Mental Maths Year 4
© A & C BLACK**

16

Zap!

- **Find the total score for zapping each pair of spaceships.**

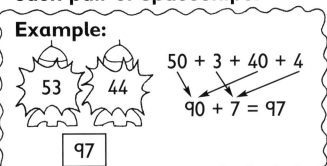

Example:

53   44

50 + 3 + 40 + 4

90 + 7 = 97

97

53   14   28
47   22
35   36   17
44   25

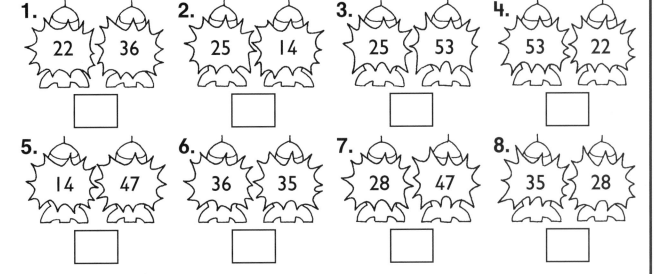

1. 22 36 ☐

2. 25 14 ☐

3. 25 53 ☐

4. 53 22 ☐

5. 14 47 ☐

6. 36 35 ☐

7. 28 47 ☐

8. 35 28 ☐

- **Write which two spaceships have been zapped.**

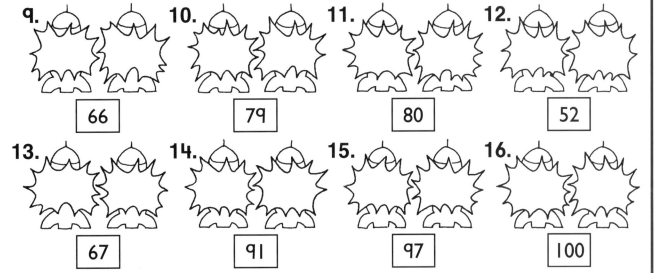

9. 66

10. 79

11. 80

12. 52

13. 67

14. 91

15. 97

16. 100

Now try this!

- **Which <u>three</u> spaceships together have a total of ☐100 ?** _____

Teachers' note Ask the children to partition the numbers into tens and units to find the totals. This can be done as jottings initially, but the children should be encouraged to do the partitioning mentally. When finding spaceships with particular totals, suggest looking at the units digits first.

**Developing Numeracy
Mental Maths Year 4
© A & C BLACK**

Hotel Costapacket

The doors in a hotel are numbered from $\boxed{1 \text{ to } 50}$.

- **Look at these two doors.**

  15 and 16 are **consecutive** numbers.

  The sum of 15 and 16 is $\boxed{31}$.

- **Find the sum of these consecutive numbers. To do this, double one of the numbers, then add or subtract 1.**

17 | 18 | 19 | 20   23 | 22 | 25 | 26

_35_

28 | 29 | 33 | 34 | 37 | 38 | 39 | 40

42 | 43 | 45 | 46 | 48 | 47 | 50 | 49

- **Write the consecutive numbers that have these sums.**

27   **33**   **49**   **55**

71   **77**   **87**   **93**

Teachers' note The children will need to know by heart or be able to derive quickly the doubles of numbers to 50. The activity on page 32 could be used to revise these facts before starting this sheet. If necessary, revise the meaning of 'consecutive'. The children could explain each calculation strategy aloud to a partner. Use a range of vocabulary to reinforce addition and doubling words.

**Developing Numeracy
Mental Maths Year 4
© A & C BLACK**

Two bees or not two bees...

- ## Play this game with a partner.

☆ **You need** a dice and two small counters (these are your 'bees').

☆ Take turns to roll the dice and move your bee. Work out the question and find the answer further along the flowerbed. Move your bee to this flower and wait until your next turn to roll the dice again.

☆ The first player to land on a beehive is the winner.

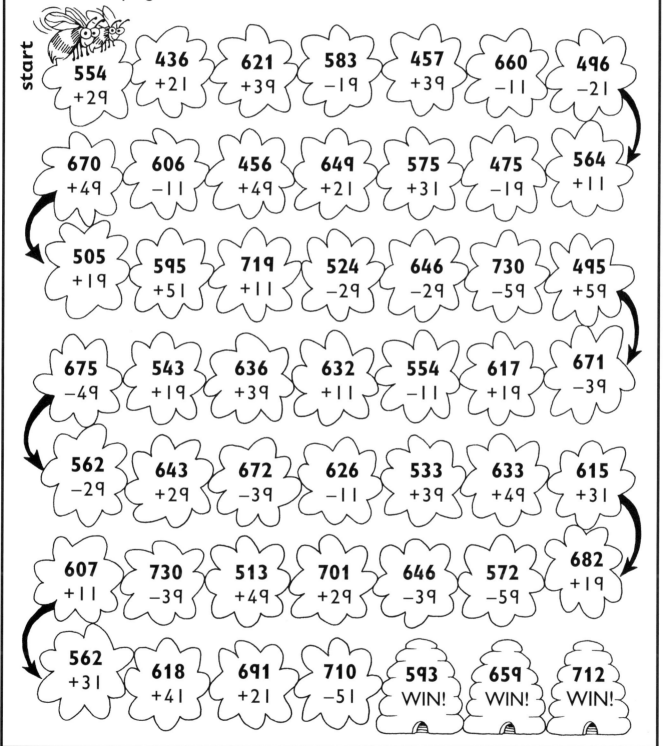

start

554 +29   436 +21   621 +39   583 −19   457 +39   660 −11   496 −21

670 +49   606 −11   456 +49   649 +21   575 +31   475 −19   564 +11

505 +19   595 +51   719 +11   524 −29   646 −29   730 −59   495 +59

675 −49   543 +19   636 +39   632 +11   554 −11   617 +19   671 −39

562 −29   643 +29   672 −39   626 −11   533 +39   633 +49   615 +31

607 +11   730 −39   513 +49   701 +29   646 −39   572 −59   682 +19

562 +31   618 +41   691 +21   710 −51   593 WIN!   659 WIN!   712 WIN!

Teachers' note Encourage the children to add or subtract a multiple of 10 and then adjust by adding or subtracting 1. As an extension activity, the children could colour in the first flower, colour the answer in the same colour, and continue until a win is reached. This can be repeated using different colours for the second and third flowers. Encourage the children to make jottings if necessary.

**Developing Numeracy
Mental Maths Year 4
© A & C BLACK**

Word hunt

Each letter of this word has a value.

T	R	I	A	N	G	L	E	S
1	2	3	4	5	6	7	8	9

- **Find the values of the words below.**

ANT $4 + 5 + 1 = 10$ RAN _____   GET _____

EGG _____   RIG _____   TEN _____

LET _____   TIN _____   SAG _____

SAT _____   LEG _____   EAR _____

RING _____   LANE _____

SELL _____   SEAT _____

REST _____   GEAR _____

NEAR _____   LINE _____

RAIN _____   LEGS _____

TRAIN _____   ANGLE _____

- **What three- or four-letter words can you find with:**

the smallest total? _____   the largest total? _____

a total of 13? _____   a total of 15? _____

a total of 18? _____   a total of 21? _____

Teachers' note Encourage the children to add the numbers in any order, and remind them to look for number pairs that total 9, 10 or 11. As a further extension, the children could find the largest five- or six-letter word totals. They could also find the sum of all the letters: show how adding the first and last numbers to make groups of ten, working inwards, can help them to find the total quickly.

**Developing Numeracy
Mental Maths Year 4
© A & C BLACK**

Greedy goat

A goat munches through the hedges in three fields.

- **What is the total angle of the three fields?**

1. 30° 50° 40° [120°]

2. 40° 70° 20° [ ]

3. 60° 60° 40° [ ]

4. 50° 40° 70° [ ]

5. 50° 90° 40° [ ]

6. 80° 70° 50° [ ]

7. 80° 90° 70° [ ]

8. 60° 70° 50° [ ]

The three angles in each triangle total [180°].

- **Fill in the missing angle.**

30° 80°

60° 60°

110° 40°

80° 70°

Teachers' note This page provides practice in totalling three multiples of 10. At this stage it is not necessary for children to know that the angles in any triangle total 180°. As a further extension, the children could write sets of three multiples of 10 that add to make 180°.

**Developing Numeracy
Mental Maths Year 4
© A & C BLACK**

Football crazy

- **Ring pairs of touching**
  horizontal numbers
  with a total of:

37	19	41	22	52	17
15	22	45	(11	28)	37
47	38	43	64	26	29
32	35	44	53	22	12

39 _11 and 28_

63 _____

69 _____

97 _____   79 _____

65 _____   85 _____

- **Ring pairs of touching**
  vertical numbers
  with a total of:

(37)	19	41	22	52	17
(15)	22	45	11	28	37
47	38	43	64	26	29
32	35	44	53	22	12

52 _37 and 15_

62 _____

80 _____

66 _____   73 _____

88 _____   117 _____

- **List all the totals you can make with pairs**
  of touching:

  horizontal numbers

  Example: 45 + 53 = 98
  53 + 58 =

  vertical numbers

  Example: 45 + 35 = 80

45	53	58	27
35	19	36	21
41	28	57	69

- **Find two pairs of non-touching numbers with a total of** 86 .

Teachers' note Discuss suitable strategies for mentally adding pairs of two-digit numbers, including using known doubles, partitioning, and adding a multiple of 10 and adjusting. Encourage the children to check using a different method, or using subtraction. For the extension activity, you could tell them that there are 17 different pairs of touching numbers in the grid.

Developing Numeracy
Mental Maths Year 4
© A & C BLACK

Phone number frenzy: 1

Here are the last six digits of a phone number.

| 5 | 7 | 1 | 3 | 2 | 8 |

In the additions below, the digits are separated by addition signs in different ways. The digits are always in the same order.

• **Find the totals.**

1. All single digits

$5 + 7 + 1 + 3 + 2 + 8 =$ _____

2. One 2-digit number

$\boxed{5\ 7} + 1 + 3 + 2 + 8 =$ _____

$5 + \boxed{7\ 1} + 3 + 2 + 8 =$ _____

$5 + 7 + \boxed{1\ 3} + 2 + 8 =$ _____

> Look! Two single digits are joined to make a 2-digit number.

$5 + 7 + 1 + \boxed{3\ 2} + 8 =$ _____

$5 + 7 + 1 + 3 + \boxed{2\ 8} =$ _____

3. Two 2-digit numbers

$\boxed{5\ 7} + \boxed{1\ 3} + 2 + 8 =$ _____

$5 + \boxed{7\ 1} + \boxed{3\ 2} + 8 =$ _____

$\boxed{5\ 7} + 1 + \boxed{3\ 2} + 8 =$ _____

$5 + 7 + \boxed{1\ 3} + \boxed{2\ 8} =$ _____

$5 + \boxed{7\ 1} + 3 + \boxed{2\ 8} =$ _____

$\boxed{5\ 7} + 1 + 3 + \boxed{2\ 8} =$ _____

4. Three 2-digit numbers

$\boxed{5\ 7} + \boxed{1\ 3} + \boxed{2\ 8} =$ _____

• **Split the digits to make one 3-digit number and three single-digit numbers. Do this in different ways and find the totals.**

Example: $5 + 7 + \boxed{1\ 3\ 2} + 8 =$ _____

> Keep the digits in the same order.

Teachers' note For the extension activity, ensure the children understand that the digits must be kept in the same order. They can continue investigations of this type using the activity on page 24. Encourage them to explain their thinking, including the strategies they used to calculate the totals mentally.

**Developing Numeracy
Mental Maths Year 4
© A & C BLACK**

Phone number frenzy: 2

- **Write any six digits here:** ☐☐☐☐☐☐

- **Now write the digits in order in the boxes below. Find the totals.**

1. All single digits

☐ + ☐ + ☐ + ☐ + ☐ + ☐ = _____

2. One 2-digit number

☐☐ + ☐ + ☐ + ☐ + ☐ = _____

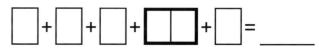

Look! Two single digits are joined to make a 2-digit number.

☐ + ☐☐ + ☐ + ☐ + ☐ = _____   ☐ + ☐ + ☐ + ☐☐ + ☐ = _____

☐ + ☐ + ☐☐ + ☐ + ☐ = _____   ☐ + ☐ + ☐ + ☐ + ☐☐ = _____

3. Two 2-digit numbers

☐☐ + ☐☐ + ☐ + ☐ = _____   ☐ + ☐ + ☐☐ + ☐☐ = _____

☐ + ☐☐ + ☐☐ + ☐ = _____   ☐ + ☐☐ + ☐ + ☐☐ = _____

☐☐ + ☐ + ☐☐ + ☐ = _____   ☐☐ + ☐ + ☐ + ☐☐ = _____

4. Three 2-digit numbers

☐☐ + ☐☐ + ☐☐ = _____

5. One 3-digit number

☐☐☐ + ☐ + ☐ + ☐ = _____   ☐ + ☐☐☐ + ☐ + ☐ = _____

☐ + ☐ + ☐☐☐ + ☐ = _____   ☐ + ☐ + ☐ + ☐☐☐ = _____

6. Two 3-digit numbers

☐☐☐ + ☐☐☐ = _____

Teachers' note The children should first complete the activity on page 23. This activity can be used to practise mental addition for a range of numbers. Ask the children to write six random digits. Keeping the digits in the same order, the children write them into the boxes and find the totals. Discuss which produces the largest total for each section.

Developing Numeracy Mental Maths Year 4 © A & C BLACK

Dinosaur Park

Doyathinkhesaurus?

- **Find the difference between the lengths of the dinosaurs.**

Seismosaurus 44 m	Diplodocus 27 m	17 m	Brachiosaurus 29 m	Apatosaurus 18 m	
Supersaurus 41 m	T. Rex 12 m		Argentinasaurus 37 m	T. Rex 12 m	
Supersaurus 41 m	Argentinasaurus 37 m		Diplodocus 27 m	T. Rex 12 m	
Diplodocus 27 m	Triceratops 9 m		Seismosaurus 44 m	Apatosaurus 18 m	
Supersaurus 41 m	Triceratops 9 m		Argentinasaurus 37 m	Triceratops 9 m	
Seismosaurus 44 m	T. Rex 12 m		Argentinasaurus 37 m	Brachiosaurus 29 m	
Seismosaurus 44 m	Triceratops 9 m		Supersaurus 41 m	Apatosaurus 18 m	

Now try this!

A school's football pitch is 82 m **long.**

- **Write the difference between the length of each dinosaur and the football pitch.**

Seismosaurus 44 m __38 m__   Argentinasaurus 37 m _____

Brachiosaurus 29 m _____   Supersaurus 41 m _____

Diplodocus 27 m _____   T. Rex 12 m _____

Apatosaurus 18 m _____   Triceratops 9 m _____

Teachers' note Encourage the children to describe the strategies they use for mentally finding the difference between two numbers less than 100 (for example, subtracting a multiple of 10 and adjusting, or using known doubles). Discuss which strategies are most effective for different questions. Some of the dinosaur lengths are estimates, as complete skeletons have not been found.

Developing Numeracy Mental Maths Year 4 © A & C BLACK

RSVP

A	B	C	D	E	F	G	H	I	J	K	L	M
7	81	31	75	56	43	92	64	38	71	15	14	78

N	O	P	Q	R	S	T	U	V	W	X	Y	Z
18	86	11	34	12	22	45	27	73	61	19	30	83

- **Work out the answers. Then find the letters in the code.**

1. $36 - 29 = \underline{7}$ [A]

2. $91 - 84 = \underline{}$

3. $82 - 71 = \underline{}$

4. $49 - 37 = \underline{}$

5. $47 - 17 = \underline{}$

6. $59 - 29 = \underline{}$

7. $84 - 57 = \underline{}$

8. $81 - 36 = \underline{}$

9. $92 - 36 = \underline{}$

10. $74 - 29 = \underline{}$

11. $81 - 59 = \underline{}$

12. $93 - 18 = \underline{}$

- **Rearrange the letters above to complete the message.**

Dear Lauren,

Please come to my ☐☐☐☐☐

on ☐☐☐☐☐☐☐.

Love from Katie RSVP

- **Fill in the missing letters from the code.**

$B - \boxed{U} = 54$ $D - \boxed{} = 14$ $G - \boxed{} = 74$

$\boxed{} - U = 29$ $\boxed{} - X = 59$ $\boxed{} - I = 48$

- **Write six letter subtractions for a partner to solve.**

Teachers' note Encourage the children to explain which number facts they used to help them answer the questions: for example, 'I know that 36 take away 30 is 6, so 36 take away 29 must be 7.' Ask the children to check their answers using an equivalent method or calculation, such as using addition to check subtractions.

**Developing Numeracy
Mental Maths Year 4
© A & C BLACK**

At the vet's

- ## Write how many pills are in each packet.

Use tables facts to find the answers.

 Felix

3 pills a day
for 7 days

| 21 | pills

 Ben

2 pills a day
for 10 days

| | pills

 Tiger

3 pills a day
for 6 days

| | pills

Tyson

5 pills a day
for 5 days

| | pills

 Jess

4 pills a day
for 7 days

| | pills

 Mitzi

1 pill a day
for 10 days

| | pills

 Cassie

5 pills a day
for 7 days

| | pills

 Nimrod

3 pills a day
for 10 days

| | pills

 Tom

2 pills a day
for 9 days

| | pills

 Fifi

3 pills a day
for 4 days

| | pills

 Pilchard

2 pills a day
for 6 days

| | pills

 Max

4 pills a day
for 5 days

| | pills

 Lassie

3 pills a day
for 9 days

| | pills

 Cleo

4 pills a day
for 4 days

| | pills

 Bruno

3 pills a day
for 8 days

| | pills

 Slinky

4 pills a day
for 8 days

| | pills

Now try this!

- ## Write your own labels for packets that contain:

| 10 pills | 12 pills | 15 pills | 32 pills | 35 pills | 40 pills |

There can be different answers to each question.

Teachers' note Ensure the children understand that these are multiplication questions from the 2, 3, 4, 5 and 10 times tables. Where possible, encourage the children to recall these facts, rather than using other counting strategies. The children could be asked to write each question as a multiplication fact: for example, for the first packet they could write 3 × 7 = 21 or 7 × 3 = 21.

**Developing Numeracy
Mental Maths Year 4
© A & C BLACK**

27

Card tricks

- **Complete this multiplication grid. Count on in equal steps along each row.**

×	1	2	3	4	5	6	7	8	9	10
1 Count in 1s	1	2	3	4	5	6	7	8	9	10
2 Count in 2s	2	4	6	8	10	12				
3 Count in 3s	3	6	9	12						
4 Count in 4s	4	8	12							
5 Count in 5s	5	10	15							
6 Count in 6s	6	12	18							
7 Count in 7s	7	14	21							
8 Count in 8s	8	16	24							
9 Count in 9s	9	18								
10 Count in 10s	10									

- **Now play this game with a partner.**

> **You need** a pack of playing cards with the picture cards removed, and a copy of this sheet <u>each</u>.

☆ Take turns to turn over two cards. Multiply the numbers.

☆ Find that question and answer in your grid. (You might be able to make two questions with your cards, such as 2×7 and 7×2.) Cross off the answer (or answers) on your grid. If you draw a cross on a grey square, have another go. If not, it is your partner's turn.

☆ Play for 10 minutes. Who crosses off the most squares?

On the grid above there is only one 64. It is the answer to the question 8×8.

- **Find other numbers that are not repeated on the grid. Write the questions for them.**

Teachers' note The children could use 1–10 number cards rather than playing cards. (They will need to keep shuffling them.) Ensure that they understand how the multiplication grid works. Discuss the symmetrical pattern and encourage the children to use this to help them check the numbers in each row. Invite them to explain why all the answers in the white squares are even.

**Developing Numeracy
Mental Maths Year 4
© A & C BLACK**

Wheels on wheels

Jo makes two 'wheels' and pins them together.

The smaller wheel spins round.

1. Write the answers to the multiplications. Then add the answers together and write the total.

(a)
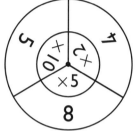

$\underline{40 + 50 + 8}$

Total _____

(b)
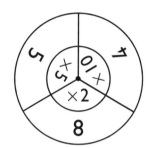

_____

Total _____

(c)
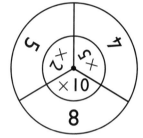

_____

Total _____

2. Do the same for these wheels.

(a)
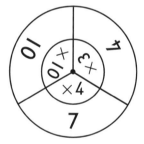

_____

Total _____

(b)
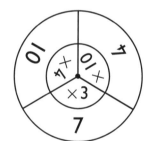

_____

Total _____

(c)
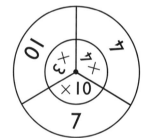

_____

Total _____

- **Cut out and pin these wheels.**
  Find all the different totals.

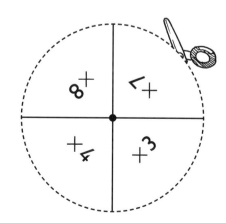
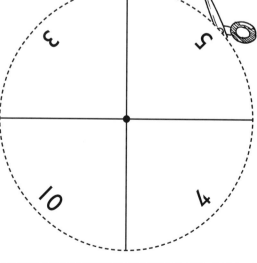

Teachers' note Ensure the children understand that they should multiply first and then find the total of the products. They will need a split pin for the extension activity. As a further extension, ask them to make their own wheels and investigate the totals. They could make wheels with more sectors (for example, eight sectors where the outer numbers are multiplied by the numbers 2 to 9).

**Developing Numeracy
Mental Maths Year 4
© A & C BLACK**

Wordsearch fun

- **Find the fruits and their scores, like this:**

☆ Ring the word. Look at the position of its first letter.

☆ Multiply the column number by the row number to get the fruit's score.

Cherry is 2 × 7 = **14**.

×	8	9	2	3	4	6	5	1	10	7
5	Y	R	R	E	B	W	A	R	T	S
9	E	M	I	L	T	A	U	Q	O	L
7	U	R	A	E	P	A	I	W	I	K
1	G	R	F	P	N	X	D	S	R	X
4	L	O	J	A	I	P	E	A	C	H
8	I	R	N	R	P	L	U	M	F	W
6	M	A	N	G	O	E	L	P	P	A
3	B	N	O	L	E	M	O	N	G	W
2	H	G	I	F	Y	R	R	E	H	C
10	S	E	A	M	U	S	T	A	S	K

cherry	14

pear	
banana	
date	
lime	
fig	

loquat	
strawberry	
lemon	
satsuma	
orange	

plum	
grape	
ugli	
apple	

peach	
mango	
melon	
kiwi	

- **Find the vegetables and their scores.**

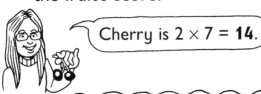

×	7	3	4	9	6	10	2	1	5	8
3	B	S	U	G	A	R	A	P	S	A
8	R	M	K	P	I	N	S	R	A	P
1	O	T	A	T	O	P	K	W	I	R
10	A	O	L	C	E	L	E	R	Y	E
2	D	R	E	A	S	W	E	D	E	B
4	B	R	O	C	C	O	L	I	F	M
9	E	A	N	P	I	N	R	U	T	U
7	A	C	I	M	A	R	R	O	W	C
5	N	T	O	O	R	T	E	E	B	U
6	M	A	N	G	E	T	O	U	T	C

turnip	45

pea	
broad bean	
broccoli	
leek	
celery	
asparagus	
carrot	
parsnip	
onion	
potato	

swede	
cucumber	

mangetout	
kale	

marrow	
beetroot	

Teachers' note This sheet could be enlarged on a photocopier, if necessary. It gives practice in tables facts up to 10 × 10. Encourage the children to use systematic methods to find the words (for example, finding all the 'a's when looking for 'apple'). As an extension, the children could be asked to make up their own wordsearch in the same style, using names of animals or countries.

Developing Numeracy Mental Maths Year 4 © A & C BLACK

Run, rabbit, run!

• **Play this game.**

You need
a dice and
a small
counter.

☆ Roll the dice and move your counter forward.

☆ Try dividing the number you land on by 2, 3, 4,
5 and 10. Which give a whole number answer?
Example: **12** ÷ 2 = 6, **12** ÷ 3 = 4, **12** ÷ 4 = 3

☆ Record the division facts on a piece of paper.
Score a point for each division fact you write.

start

12	9	18	36	10	27

21

24	16	8	17	15	30

25

14	35	50	23	20	6

40

finish

26	52	39	32	45	28

• **Play the game again. Can you get a higher score?**

• **Which number between 18 and 35 is a multiple of:**

2, 3, 5 and 10?   2, 3 and 4?   2, 4, 5 and 10?

Teachers' note The children should work individually for this activity. Emphasise that they should record only the division facts with whole number answers. Ensure the children appreciate that if a whole number answer can be found, then the number is a multiple: for example, 12 ÷ 2 = 6, so 12 is a multiple of 2. This activity can lead on to looking at remainders.

Developing Numeracy
Mental Maths Year 4
© A & C BLACK

Doubling machine

This machine doubles numbers.

First it splits the number.

Then it doubles each part.

Finally, it adds them together.

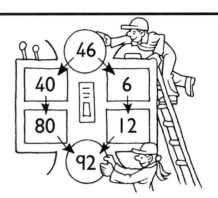

• Use the machine to double numbers between ⬜10 and ⬜50.

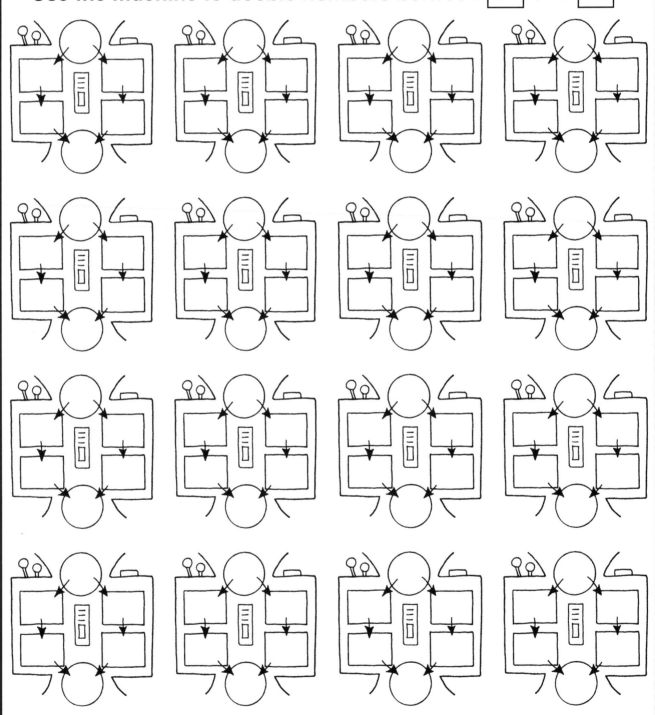

Teachers' note This activity helps the children to double numbers to 50, and to memorise them. Explain that the machine splits the number into tens and units. The numbers could be filled in before photocopying (including numbers ending in 5, 6, 7, 8 or 9, where the double of the units digit gives a two-digit number). Alternatively, the children can choose numbers, or generate them by rolling a dice.

Developing Numeracy
Mental Maths Year 4
© A & C BLACK

Halving links

- **Follow these rules to make number chains.**

☆ Start with an **even** number from 20 to 100.

☆ Halve the number, then add 4.

☆ Keep going until you reach an **odd** number.

The Great HOUDINI

Half 84 = 42, 42 + 4 = 46...

84) 46) 27 ◄— odd   96) 52) 30) 19 ◄— odd

84 has **three links**   96 has **four links**

- **Choose your own start numbers from 20 to 100.**

What are the longest and shortest chains you can make?

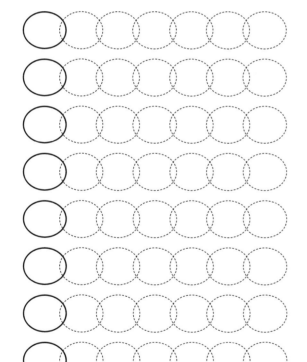

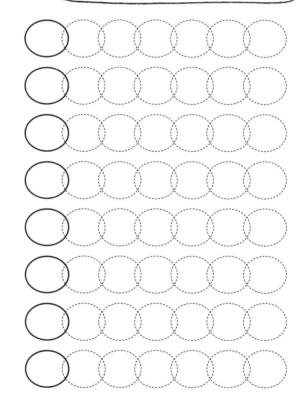

- **Can you find a number that has seven links?** _____

Now try this!

- **Find all the start numbers from 20 to 100 that have only two links in the chain.**

38 has two links.

- **What do you notice?**

Teachers' note This activity involves halving even numbers to 100. Begin the lesson by practising doubles of numbers to 50 and remind the children that halving is the inverse (opposite) of doubling. Go through the rules of the activity carefully, reminding the children how to recognise odd and even numbers.

Developing Numeracy
Mental Maths Year 4
© A & C BLACK

There and back again

The distances between cities are shown.

• Double the distances to find the number of miles in a round trip.

Miss Detrain Coach Tours

1. London to:

	Hull 210 miles	Cologne 330 miles	Paris 220 miles
Round trip	_420_ miles	_____ miles	_____ miles

2. Newcastle to:

	Liverpool 160 miles	Leicester 190 miles	London 270 miles
Round trip	_____ miles	_____ miles	_____ miles

3. Geneva to:

	Vienna 500 miles	Rome 440 miles	Paris 240 miles
Round trip	_____ miles	_____ miles	_____ miles

4. Vienna to:

	Cologne 450 miles	Hamburg 470 miles	Rome 480 miles
Round trip	_____ miles	_____ miles	_____ miles

5. Glasgow to:

	Colchester 390 miles	Cardiff 370 miles	Bristol 360 miles
Round trip	_____ miles	_____ miles	_____ miles

Now try this!

• **How far is a one-way trip, if the round trip is:**

	460 miles?	580 miles?	760 miles?	920 miles?
One way	_____ miles	_____ miles	_____ miles	_____ miles

Teachers' note At the start of the lesson, describe the questions using vocabulary such as: 'What is double 160? What is twice 440? How many is 220 add 220?' Encourage the children to use known facts, such as 27 + 27 for finding double 270. During the plenary, invite them to say how they worked out the answers or whether they have learned the doubles and corresponding halves by heart.

**Developing Numeracy
Mental Maths Year 4
© A & C BLACK**

World trips

Here are the distances of one-way flights between cities.

• **Double the distances to find the total for a round trip.**

1.

Cairo ●——— 4600 km ———● Beijing
Cairo ●——— 2700 km ———● Mumbai
Cairo ●——— 3500 km ———● Cape Town

Round trip from Cairo to:

Mumbai <u>5400</u> km   Cape Town _____ km   Beijing _____ km

2.

Baghdad ●——— 4900 km ———● Cape Town
Baghdad ●——— 1800 km ———● Vienna
Baghdad ●——— 3900 km ———● Calcutta

Round trip from Baghdad to:

Vienna _____ km   Calcutta _____ km   Cape Town _____ km

3.

Chicago ●——— 4700 km ———● Vienna
Chicago ●——— 1900 km ———● San Francisco
Chicago ●——— 4200 km ———● Cologne

Round trip from Chicago to:

San Francisco _____ km   Cologne _____ km   Vienna _____ km

4.

Athens ●——— 4800 km ———● Ottawa
Athens ●——— 1600 km ———● Oslo
Athens ●——— 2800 km ———● Nairobi

Round trip from Athens to:

Oslo _____ km   Nairobi _____ km   Ottawa _____ km

These are the distances of round trips from Calcutta.

Hong Kong 3400 km   Istanbul 7200 km   Darwin 7400 km

• **Find the one-way distance to each city.**

Teachers' note As a further extension, the children could be asked to find information about distances between other cities. They should round the distances to the nearest 100 km. Puzzle cards can then be made of the information for future doubling practice.

Developing Numeracy
Mental Maths Year 4
© A & C BLACK

You've been framed

Zoë takes four pieces of wood. She cuts the corners to shape and joins the pieces to make a frame.

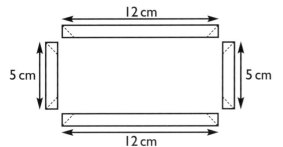
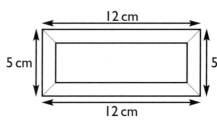

total length **34 cm**

• **Use doubling to find the total length of wood needed for each frame.**

1.
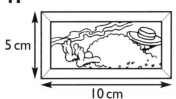
5 cm
10 cm

total length _____ cm

2.
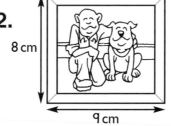
8 cm
9 cm

total length _____ cm

3.

9 cm
7 cm

total length _____ cm

4.
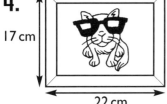
17 cm
22 cm

total length _____ cm

5.
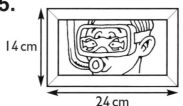
14 cm
24 cm

total length _____ cm

6.
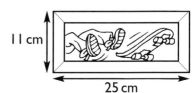
11 cm
25 cm

total length _____ cm

7.
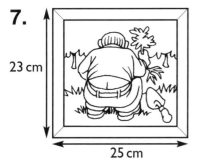
23 cm
25 cm

total length _____ cm

8.
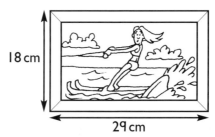
18 cm
29 cm

total length _____ cm

9.
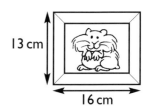
13 cm
16 cm

total length _____ cm

• **Zoë uses exactly** 92 cm **of wood. Write the length and width of different frames she could make.**

Teachers' note Demonstrate different approaches to solving these problems, such as adding the length and width and doubling the answer, or doubling each measurement and then adding them. Ask the children to say which approach they find easier and discourage the strategy of adding all four numbers. The activity on page 32 can be used for further practice in doubling numbers to 50.

**Developing Numeracy
Mental Maths Year 4
© A & C BLACK**

Doubling towers

- **Double the arrow number in the question and double the answer to make a new fact. Keep going.**

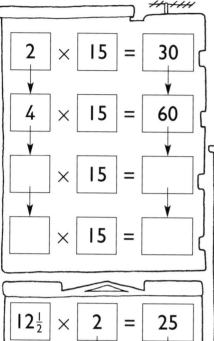

2	×	15	=	30
4	×	15	=	60
	×	15	=	
	×	15	=	

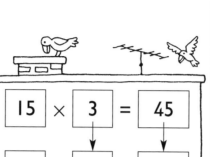

5	×	6	=	30
	×		=	
	×		=	

15	×	3	=	45
15	×	6	=	
	×		=	
	×		=	
	×		=	

$12\frac{1}{2}$	×	2	=	25
$12\frac{1}{2}$	×		=	
	×		=	
	×		=	
	×		=	

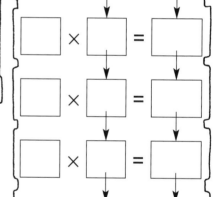

13	×	2	=	26
	×		=	
	×		=	
	×		=	
	×		=	

Now try this!

- **Work out these answers in your head.**

Remember: to multiply a number by 2, **double**

to multiply a number by 4, **double, double**

to multiply a number by 8, **double, double, double.**

$14 \times 2 =$ _____ $6 \times 4 =$ _____ $15 \times 8 =$ _____ $21 \times 4 =$ _____

$32 \times 2 =$ _____ $31 \times 4 =$ _____ $6 \times 8 =$ _____ $8 \times 8 =$ _____

Teachers' note Practise doubling strategies at the start of the lesson. The children will need to be confident in knowing, or being able to derive, doubles of numbers to 50, doubles of multiples of 5 and doubles of multiples of 50. Encourage the children to check doubling by halving, and vice versa.

**Developing Numeracy
Mental Maths Year 4
© A & C BLACK**

Secret trails

- **Use this key to complete the calculation trails below.**

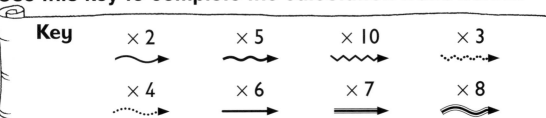

Key

× 2, × 5, × 10, × 3
× 4, × 6, × 7, × 8

3 → 15 → 30 → 90 → 900

2 → ○ → ○ → ○ → ○

4 → ○ → ○ → ○ → ○

2 → ○ → ○ → ○ → ○ → ○

1 → ○ → ○ → ○ → ○ → ○

5 → ○ → ○ → ○ → ○ → ○

2 → ○ → ○ → ○ → ○ → ○

1 → ○ → ○ → ○ → ○ → ○

3 → ○ → ○ → ○ → ○ → ○

- **Make up four secret trails of your own. Give them to a partner to solve.**

Teachers' note This activity provides practice in multiplying and doubling (including multiplying single digits by multiples of 10 and 100). Remind the children to look carefully at the different styles of arrows. For the extension activity, they could use the same key or make their own colour key. Stress that they must be able to work out each of the answers mentally.

Developing Numeracy Mental Maths Year 4 © A & C BLACK

Secret trails tips

• **Look at this key.**

Key	× 2	× 3	× 4	× 6	× 8

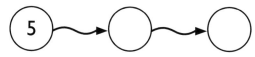

1. Use the key to find the end numbers for these trails.

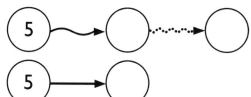

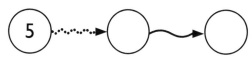

Discuss with a partner what you notice.
Use this to help you answer these questions.

15 × 4 = ☐   13 × 4 = ☐   24 × 4 = ☐   35 × 4 = ☐

2. Use the key to find the end numbers for these trails.

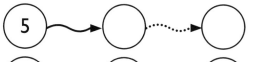

Discuss with a partner what you notice.
Use this to help you answer these questions.

15 × 6 = ☐   12 × 6 = ☐   25 × 6 = ☐   35 × 6 = ☐

3. Use the key to find the end numbers for these trails.

Discuss with a partner what you notice.
Use this to help you answer these questions.

7 × 8 = ☐   12 × 8 = ☐   15 × 8 = ☐   25 × 8 = ☐

• **How can you use the key to multiply the number ☐ 5**
by 12? Draw six different trails.

Example: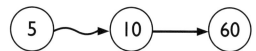

Teachers' note The children should first complete the activity on page 38 so that they are familiar with the arrows in the key and the format of the trails. This activity helps them to appreciate that multiplications do not have to be done all in one step, or in any particular order. Encourage the children to look for the easiest way to multiply mentally for each question.

Developing Numeracy
Mental Maths Year 4
© A & C BLACK

Key to success

- **Complete these patterns. Multiply by 10 first, then use this to help you work out the other answers.**

$14 \times 9 =$ 126
$14 \times 10 =$ 140
$14 \times 11 =$ 154

$21 \times 9 =$
$21 \times 10 =$ 210
$21 \times 11 =$

$25 \times 9 =$
$25 \times 10 =$
$25 \times 11 =$

$34 \times 9 =$
$34 \times 10 =$
$34 \times 11 =$

$43 \times 9 =$
$43 \times 10 =$
$43 \times 11 =$

$52 \times 9 =$
$52 \times 10 =$
$52 \times 11 =$

$54 \times 9 =$
$54 \times 10 =$
$54 \times 11 =$

$17 \times 9 =$
$17 \times 10 =$
$17 \times 11 =$

$26 \times 9 =$
$26 \times 10 =$
$26 \times 11 =$

$35 \times 9 =$
$35 \times 10 =$
$35 \times 11 =$

$29 \times 9 =$
$29 \times 10 =$
$29 \times 11 =$

$48 \times 9 =$
$48 \times 10 =$
$48 \times 11 =$

$81 \times 9 =$
$81 \times 10 =$
$81 \times 11 =$

$99 \times 9 =$
$99 \times 10 =$
$99 \times 11 =$

Now try this!

- **To answer these questions, multiply the first number by 10, then add or subtract to find the answer.**

$32 \times 11 =$ _____ $18 \times 11 =$ _____ $31 \times 11 =$ _____

$41 \times 11 =$ _____ $51 \times 11 =$ _____ $47 \times 11 =$ _____

$56 \times 9 =$ _____ $44 \times 9 =$ _____ $19 \times 9 =$ _____

$53 \times 9 =$ _____ $75 \times 9 =$ _____ $84 \times 9 =$ _____

Teachers' note Demonstrate this strategy at the start of the lesson. Show that to multiply a number by 9 we can multiply by 10 and then subtract the number. To multiply a number by 11 we can multiply by 10 and then add the number. The children can check their answers by making sure that the three answers in each set go up in steps of equal size (the size of the first number in the question).

**Developing Numeracy
Mental Maths Year 4
© A & C BLACK**

40

Giant waffles

- **Use multiplication to find the number of squares on each waffle.**

1. 4×13

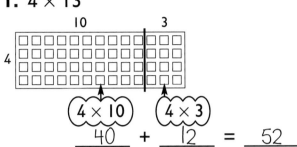

$$40 + 12 = 52$$

Some are covered with cream!

2. 5×16

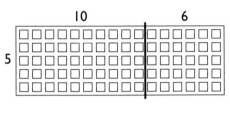

_____ + _____ = _____

3. 4×17

_____ + _____ = _____

4. 8×16

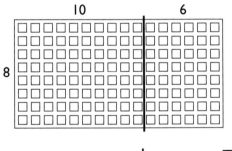

_____ + _____ = _____

5. 8×26

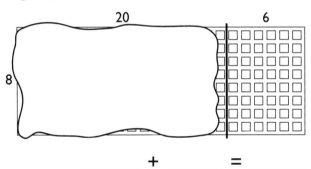

_____ + _____ = _____

6. 8×24

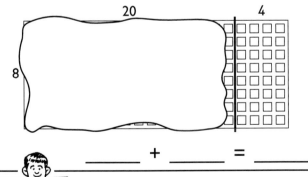

_____ + _____ = _____

7. 6×23

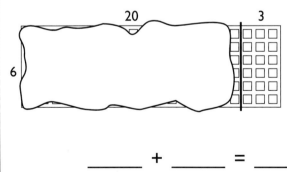

_____ + _____ = _____

Now try this! • **Use the same method to answer these.**

$5 \times 14 =$ _____ $4 \times 19 =$ _____ $3 \times 21 =$ _____ $7 \times 23 =$ _____

$3 \times 26 =$ _____ $4 \times 29 =$ _____ $6 \times 26 =$ _____ $8 \times 27 =$ _____

Teachers' note Before beginning, discuss different ways of finding the number of squares on each waffle, including counting rows or columns. Show how partitioning can be used to reach answers more quickly. This sheet can also be used to introduce the grid method of multiplication.

**Developing Numeracy
Mental Maths Year 4
© A & C BLACK**

Machine magic

In these machines, only one 'input' number gives the same 'output' number.

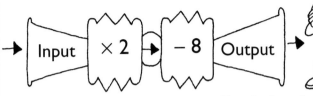

→ | Input | × 2 | → | − 8 | Output | →

Input	Output
5	2
6	4
7	6
⑧	⑧
9	10
10	12

• For each machine, find the input number that gives the same output. Choose input numbers between 5 and 10.

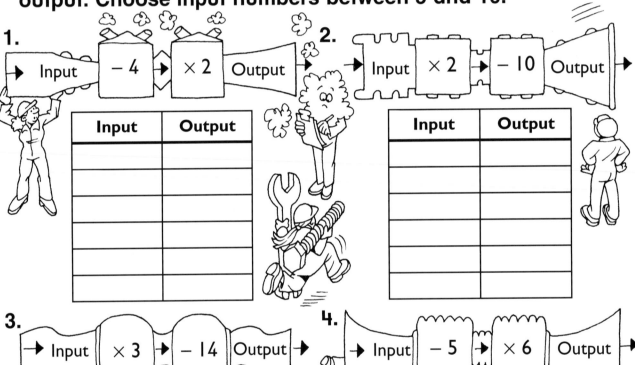

1.

→ Input | − 4 | → | × 2 | Output →

Input	Output

2.

→ Input | × 2 | → | − 10 | Output →

Input	Output

3.

→ Input | × 3 | → | − 14 | Output →

Input	Output

4.

→ Input | − 5 | → | × 6 | Output →

Input	Output

• **Make up three machines of your own which start with** ×2 **. Find the number that stays the same.**

Developing Numeracy
Mental Maths Year 4
© A & C BLACK

Teachers' note Ensure the children realise that for each machine, only one input number will produce the same output number. For the extension activity, some children may need a number line that includes negative numbers (for example, '× 2 − 12' would produce the output number ⁻2 for the input number 5).

Fractious pirates

- **Use division to work out the numbers of pirates.**

1. There were ⟨40⟩ pirates on the *Ghastly Galleon*.

$\frac{1}{2}$ were seasick _____ 40 ÷ 2 = 20 pirates

$\frac{1}{4}$ had wooden legs _____

$\frac{1}{5}$ were drowned _____

$\frac{1}{10}$ walked the plank _____

2. There were ⟨24⟩ pirates on the *Jolly Marauder*.

$\frac{1}{2}$ had beards _____

$\frac{1}{4}$ were homesick _____

$\frac{1}{8}$ owned a parrot _____

$\frac{1}{3}$ hated ship's biscuits _____

$\frac{1}{6}$ wore earrings _____

3. There were ⟨36⟩ pirates on the *Buccaneer*.

$\frac{1}{2}$ had scurvy _____

$\frac{1}{4}$ fell overboard _____

$\frac{1}{9}$ owned a cat _____

$\frac{1}{3}$ ate a maggoty biscuit _____

$\frac{1}{6}$ had eye patches _____

- **Make up puzzles about the pirates on these ships.**

Now try this!

the *Revenge*
60 pirates

the *Black Shark*
48 pirates

Teachers' note Remind the children that to find $\frac{1}{2}$, $\frac{1}{4}$, $\frac{1}{5}$ and so on, they should divide by the bottom number of the fraction. For the extension activity, point out that they must only use fractions that give whole numbers of pirates. As a further extension, the children could write their own puzzle cards for mental practice of division in the classroom.

**Developing Numeracy
Mental Maths Year 4
© A & C BLACK**

Real or fake?

Which diamonds are real and which are fake?

- **Divide each number on the left by the number diagonally opposite. If the answers are the same, the diamond is <u>real</u>.**
- **Write real or fake next to each diamond.**

1.
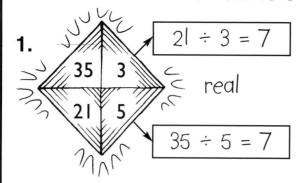

$21 \div 3 = 7$

real

$35 \div 5 = 7$

2.
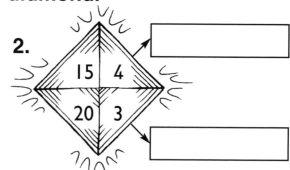

3.
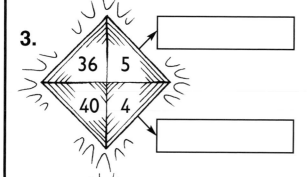

4.
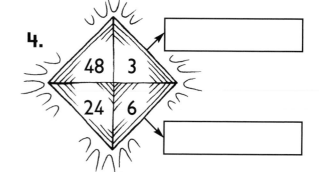

5.
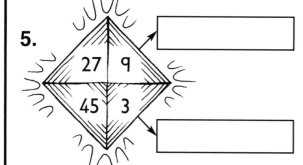

6.
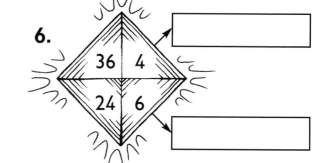

7.
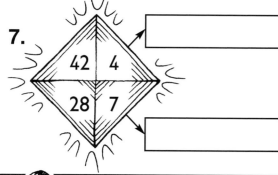

8.
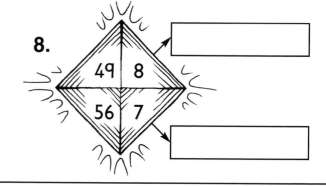

- **Make up three <u>real</u> diamonds of your own.**

Teachers' note Revise division facts corresponding to the times tables at the start of the lesson. Some children may need a list of the tables/division facts to refer to if they do not know them by heart. Ensure the children understand the meaning of 'diagonally opposite'. For the extension activity, they could make diamond cards to be used as a practical classroom resource.

Developing Numeracy
Mental Maths Year 4
© A & C BLACK

Remainder game

• **Play this game with a partner.**

☆ Cut out the cards. Place them in a pile, face down.

☆ Take turns to pick up a card. Answer the question, giving a remainder.

☆ Score the same number of points as the remainder.

   Example: 21 ÷ 5 = 4 r 1   Score 1 point.

☆ Write down your score.

☆ Continue until all the cards are used up. The winner is the player with the **fewest** points.

21 ÷ 5	23 ÷ 5	25 ÷ 3	15 ÷ 2
11 ÷ 2	17 ÷ 4	19 ÷ 4	24 ÷ 5
20 ÷ 3	26 ÷ 4	29 ÷ 5	18 ÷ 5
24 ÷ 10	35 ÷ 4	31 ÷ 5	42 ÷ 10
43 ÷ 5	23 ÷ 3	32 ÷ 10	14 ÷ 5
9 ÷ 2	15 ÷ 4	37 ÷ 5	26 ÷ 3
44 ÷ 10	22 ÷ 3	26 ÷ 5	47 ÷ 5
48 ÷ 5	27 ÷ 4	33 ÷ 5	17 ÷ 2
39 ÷ 5	64 ÷ 10	38 ÷ 5	74 ÷ 10

Teachers' note At the start of the lesson, provide practice in using tables facts to find answers to questions with remainders. Keep the children focused on the remainder part of the calculation. As an extension activity, ask the children to group the cards into sets with the same remainder.

**Developing Numeracy
Mental Maths Year 4
© A & C BLACK**

Hamster homework

Harry the hamster has nibbled this homework.

- **Fill in the missing numbers in the number facts.**

1. $150 \div 2 =$ 75

2. $90 \div 10 =$

3. $6 \times$ $= 18$

4. $10 \times$ $= 230$

5. $\div 5 = 3$

6. $\div 4 = 10$

7. $5 \times 12 =$

8. $4 \times 8 =$

9. $24 \div$ $= 8$

10. $25 \div$ $= 5$

11. $\times 5 = 35$

12. $\times 4 = 28$

13. $70 \div 2 =$

14. $170 \div 2 =$

15. $15 \times$ $= 150$

16. $6 \times$ $= 24$

17. $\div 5 = 8$

18. $\div 4 = 4$

- **Write two division and two multiplication puzzles of your own. Give them to a partner to solve.**

$\div$ ___ = ___ $\div$ ___ = ___

$\times$ ___ = ___ $\times$ ___ = ___

Teachers' note These mixed questions require children to know or be able to derive tables and division facts, and doubles of multiples of 5 up to 100 and the corresponding halves. Encourage the children to discuss their answers with a partner and to explain how they calculated each one. They should check their answers using inverse operations.

**Developing Numeracy
Mental Maths Year 4
© A & C BLACK**

46

Answers

p 6
1. + 1000	**2.** + 10	**3.** − 100
4. + 1	**5.** − 1000	**6.** − 1
7. + 100	**8.** + 10	**9.** + 1
10. − 100	**11.** − 10	**12.** + 1000

p 7
1.
200p	500p	900p
3400p	2700p	4800p
12 100p	26 000p	30 600p

2.
400 cm	700 cm	800 cm
6200 cm	7400 cm	9700 cm
63 000 cm	10 500 cm	63 000 cm

Now try this!
£4	£6	£11
£67	£83	£953
25 m	53 m	49 m
664 m	101 m	220 m

p 8
Now try this!
<	>	>
7470, 7480	5000, 5010, 5020	7990, 8000, 8010
>	>	<
2100, 2110, 2120	7680, 7690, 7700	3080, 3090, 3100

p 9
1. 80 cm   **2.** 84 cm   **3.** 81 cm

Now try this!
67 cm

p 10
Now try this!
325 km

p 11
Now try this!
child	adult	adult
child	child	adult

p 12
8	16	13
16	15	14
12	18	18
15	19	19
20	20	17
19	20	18

p 13
18 − 4 = 14
20 − 9 = 11
14 − 7 = 7
12 − 1 = 11
16 − 7 = 9
17 − 10 = 7
19 − 3 = 16
20 − 6 = 14
17 − 9 = 8
17 − 4 = 13
12 − 3 = 9
16 − 5 = 11
20 − 3 = 17
19 − 5 = 14
18 − 9 = 9

1. 13	**2.** 8	**3.** 7	**4.** 11
5. 13	**6.** 15	**7.** 9	**8.** 7

p 14
Now try this!
27	69	12
56	38	23
64	57	72

p 15
1. 850 ml	**2.** 700 ml	**3.** 50 ml
4. 250 ml	**5.** 200 ml	**6.** 450 ml
7. 650 ml	**8.** 750 ml	**9.** 950 ml
10. 600 ml	**11.** 300 ml	**12.** 550 ml

Now try this!
Nineteen possible answers where numbers are multiples of 50p and have a total of £10, e.g. 50p and £9.50.

p 16
15 m	7 m
9 m	10 m
14 m	12 m
18 m	18 m
22 m	21 m
23 m	24 m
27 m	26 m
24 m	29 m

p 17
1. 58	**2.** 39	**3.** 78	**4.** 75
5. 61	**6.** 71	**7.** 75	**8.** 63
9. 44, 22	**10.** 44, 35	**11.** 44, 36	**12.** 35, 17
13. 14, 53	**14.** 47, 44	**15.** 53, 44	**16.** 53, 47

Now try this!
47 + 17 + 36 **or** 22 + 25 + 53 **or** 25 + 28 + 47

p 18
35	39	45	51
57	67	75	79
85	91	95	99

Now try this!
13, 14	16, 17	24, 25	27, 28
35, 36	38, 39	43, 44	46, 47

p 20
10	11	15
20	11	14
16	9	19
14	21	14

16	24
31	22
20	20
19	23
14	30
15	30

Now try this!
Example answers:
RAT, ART (7)	LESS (33)
ATE	NAG
GAIN	SALT

p 21
1. 120°	**2.** 130°
3. 160°	**4.** 160°
5. 180°	**6.** 200°
7. 240°	**8.** 180°

Now try this!
70°	60°	30°	30°

p 22
11 and 28	
41 and 22	
52 and 17	
44 and 53	35 and 44
28 and 37	47 and 38
37 and 15	
15 and 47	
52 and 28	
37 and 29	38 and 35
45 and 43	64 and 53

Now try this!
Horizontal totals: 98, 111, 85, 54, 55, 57, 69, 85, 126
Vertical totals: 80, 72, 94, 48, 76, 47, 93, 90

45 + 41 = 86   58 + 28 = 86

p 23
1. 26
2. 71

89	53
35	44

3. 80 53

116	107
98	89

4. 98

Now try this!
571 + 3 + 2 + 8 = 584   5 + 713 + 2 + 8 = 728
5 + 7 + 132 + 8 = 152   5 + 7 + 1 + 328 = 341

p 25

17 m	11 m
29 m	25 m
4 m	15 m
18 m	26 m
32 m	28 m
32 m	8 m
35 m	23 m

Now try this!

38 m	45 m
53 m	41 m
55 m	70 m
64 m	73 m

p 26
1. 7 [A]   **2.** 7 [A]   **3.** 11 [P]   **4.** 12 [R]
5. 30 [Y]   **6.** 30 [Y]   **7.** 27 [U]   **8.** 45 [T]
9. 56 [E]   **10.** 45 [T]   **11.** 22 [S]   **12.** 75 [D]

PARTY, TUESDAY

Now try this!

U	W	N
E	M	O

p 28
Now try this!
1 × 1 = 1   5 × 5 = 25   7 × 7 = 49
8 × 8 = 64   9 × 9 = 81   10 × 10 = 100

p 29
1. (a) 40 + 50 + 8 = 98   **2. (a)** 28 + 100 + 12 = 140
(b) 16 + 25 + 40 = 81   **(b)** 21 + 40 + 40 = 101
(c) 80 + 10 + 20 = 110   **(c)** 70 + 30 + 16 = 116

p 30

cherry	14	loquat	63	plum	32
pear	28	strawberry	35	grape	18
banana	24	lemon	9	ugli	56
date	5	satsuma	100	apple	42
lime	27	orange	36	peach	24
fig	6			mango	48
				melon	18
				kiwi	49

turnip	45	asparagus	24	swede	12
pea	10	carrot	21	cucumber	48
broad bean	21	parsnip	64	mangetout	42
broccoli	28	onion	16	kale	32
leek	8	potato	10	marrow	63
celery	90			beetroot	25

p 31
Now try this!
30   24   20

p 33
72 has seven links.

Now try this!
They are all even numbers that are two greater than a multiple of 4,
i.e. 22, 26, 30, 34, 38, 42, 46, 50, 54… 98

p 34
1. 420 miles   660 miles   440 miles
2. 320 miles   380 miles   540 miles
3. 1000 miles   880 miles   480 miles
4. 900 miles   940 miles   960 miles
5. 780 miles   740 miles   720 miles

Now try this!
230 miles   290 miles   380 miles   460 miles

p 35
1. 5400 km   7000 km   9200 km
2. 3600 km   7800 km   9800 km
3. 3800 km   8400 km   9400 km
4. 3200 km   5600 km   9600 km

Now try this!
1700 km   3600 km   3700 km

p 36
1. 30 cm   **2.** 34 cm   **3.** 32 cm
4. 78 cm   **5.** 76 cm   **6.** 72 cm
7. 96 cm   **8.** 94 cm   **9.** 58 cm

p 37
Now try this!

28	24	120	84
64	124	48	64

p 38

3	15	30	90	900	
2	8	40	80	800	
4	16	32	320	640	
2	6	30	240	480	4800
1	5	35	70	280	560
5	30	120	240	2400	4800
2	4	8	40	160	1600
1	7	21	42	420	840
3	6	18	36	360	720

p 39

60	52	96	140
90	72	150	210
56	96	120	200

p 40

126	189	
140	210	
154	231	
225	306	387
250	340	430
275	374	473
468	486	153
520	540	170
572	594	187
234	315	261
260	350	290
286	385	319
432	729	891
480	810	990
528	891	1089

Now try this!

352	198	341
451	561	517
504	396	171
477	675	756

p 41
1. 52
2. 80   **3.** 68
4. 128   **5.** 208
6. 192   **7.** 138

Now try this!

70	76	63	161
78	116	156	216

p 42
1. 8   **2.** 10   **3.** 7   **4.** 6

p 43
1. 20 10 8   4
2. 12 6   3   8   4
3. 18 9   4   12 6

p 44
The diamonds in questions 1, 2, 4, 6 and 8 are 'real'.

p 46
1. 75   **2.** 9   **3.** 3   **4.** 23
5. 15   **6.** 40   **7.** 60   **8.** 32
9. 3   **10.** 5   **11.** 7   **12.** 7
13. 35   **14.** 85   **15.** 10   **16.** 4
17. 40   **18.** 16